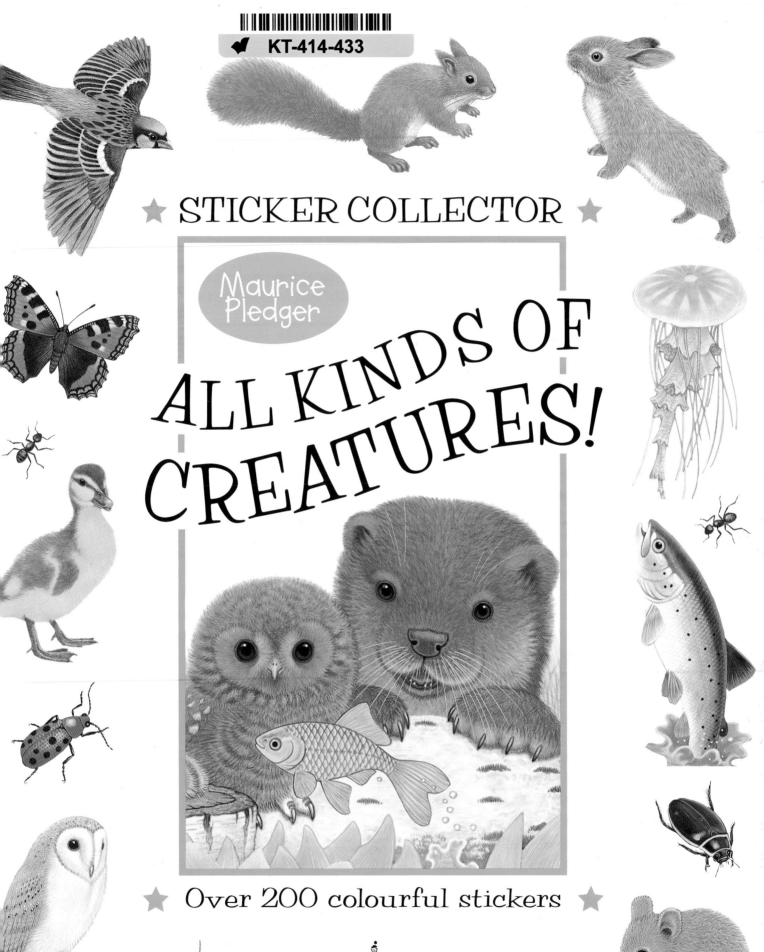

★ STICKER COLLECTOR ★

Maurice Pledger

ALL KINDS OF CREATURES!

★ Over 200 colourful stickers ★

templar publishing

All kinds of CREATURES

The world is full of all kinds of creatures. Some have fur or feathers. Some have wings or beaks or shells. Here you can see Oscar Otter and his friend Dilly Dormouse. They are both **mammals**. On Oscar's back you can see Ozzy Owl and Sally Cygnet. They are both **birds**.
What other creatures can you see in the picture?

Can you see a butterfly? Or a beetle? Butterflies and beetles both belong to a group of animals called **insects**. On the following pages you can find out about the most common groups of animals that live in our world. You'll meet all sorts of wonderful creatures and don't forget to use your stickers as you go!

★ All sorts of INSECTS

Down in the meadow Billy Bunny and his friend Charlie Chick have found all sorts of insects. You can find out their names over the page. Use your stickers to add a flying beetle and a honey bee to the picture.

Beetles, bees and other insects

Charlie Chick loves to go looking for insects. You can see lots of different ones here. Look for them in your garden, especially in the summer.

Beetles

Use your stickers to fill in the shapes with the right insect. You can fill them all in now or wait until you see each different type of creature.

Bumble bees

Honey bee

Hoverfly

Wasp

Beeflies

Flies

Grasshoppers

Other creepy-crawlies

Apart from insects, there are lots of other creepy-crawly creatures. Do you already know the names of some of the ones shown here?

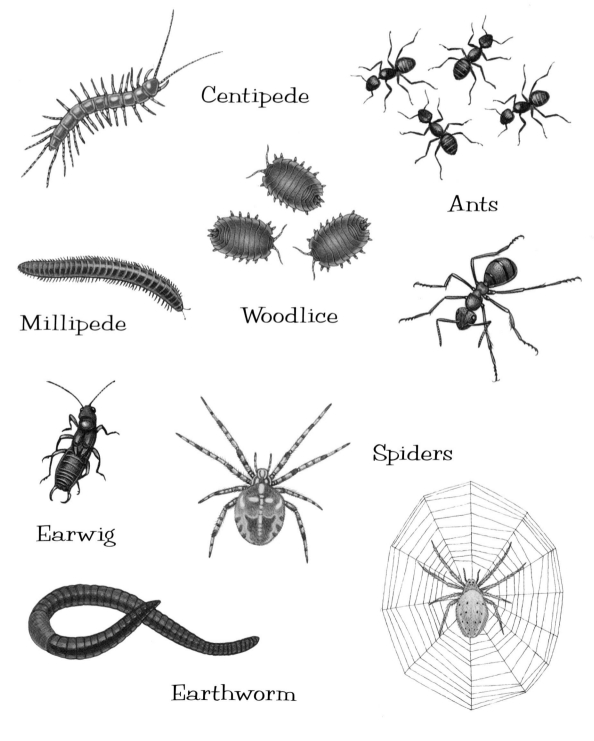

Centipede

Ants

Woodlice

Millipede

Spiders

Earwig

Earthworm

Say the creepy-crawlies' names as you fill in the shapes with the right stickers.

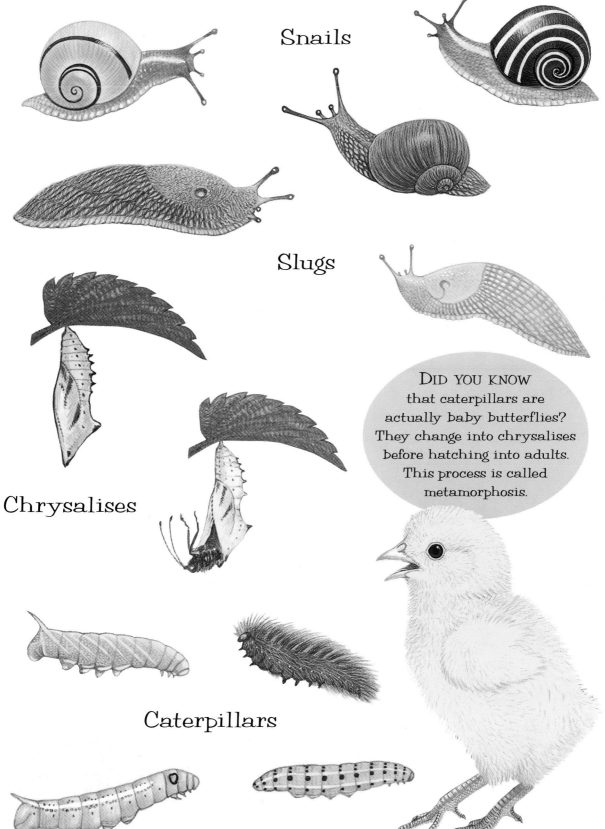

Snails

Slugs

Chrysalises

DID YOU KNOW
that caterpillars are
actually baby butterflies?
They change into chrysalises
before hatching into adults.
This process is called
metamorphosis.

Caterpillars

Butterflies and moths

Butterflies and moths are some of the most colourful insects of all. Their wings are often covered in fantastic patterns.

Butterflies

Use your stickers to fill in these shapes with different butterflies and moths.

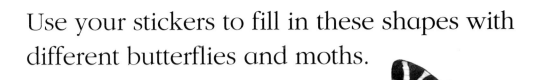

Moths

DID YOU KNOW that most moths fly at night. But the cinnabar moth (below) flies during the day!

Pond insects

Pond
snail

Water
boatman

Great
diving beetle

Ramshorn
snail

Some insects and creepy-crawlies only live
in or by the water. Add another water
beetle and a pond snail to this picture.

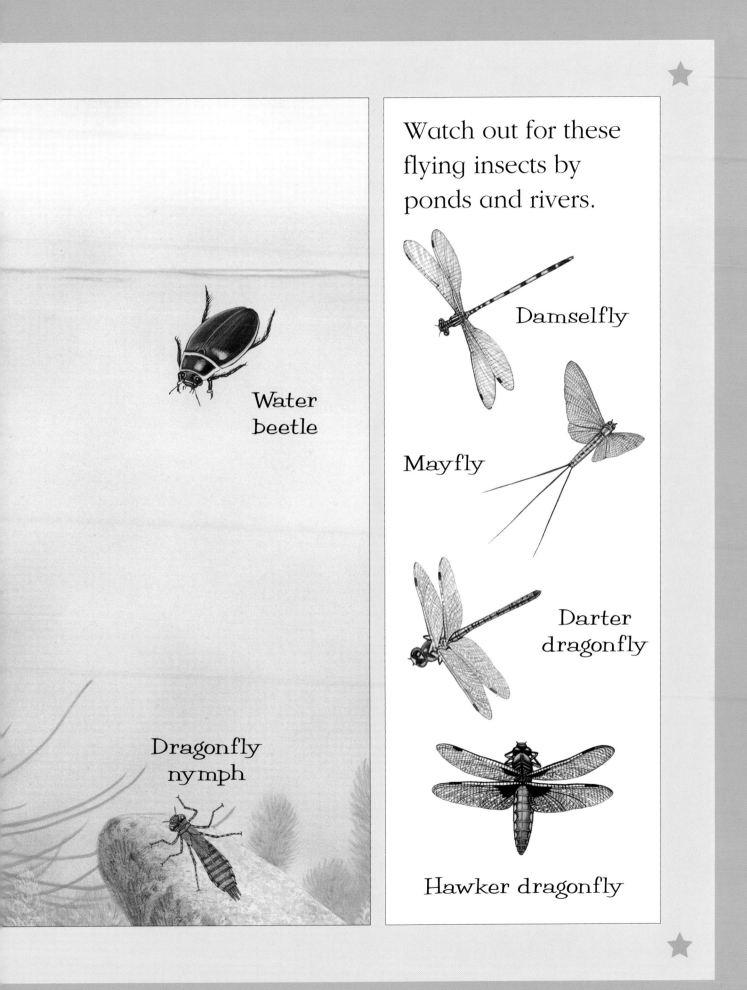

Water
beetle

Dragonfly
nymph

Watch out for these
flying insects by
ponds and rivers.

Damselfly

Mayfly

Darter
dragonfly

Hawker dragonfly

REPTILES and AMPHIBIANS

Oscar Otter and Duggy Duckling are looking
for two other sorts of creature by the river – reptiles
and amphibians. Find out about them over the page,
then add another frog and a terrapin to the picture.

Snakes, frogs and other friends

Look at the different reptiles and amphibians that Oscar Otter and Duggy have found. Use your stickers to fill in their shapes.

Lizard

Tortoise

These creatures are all reptiles.

Turtle

Terrapin

Snake

18

Reptiles and amphibians both lay eggs. Frogs' eggs are called frogspawn.

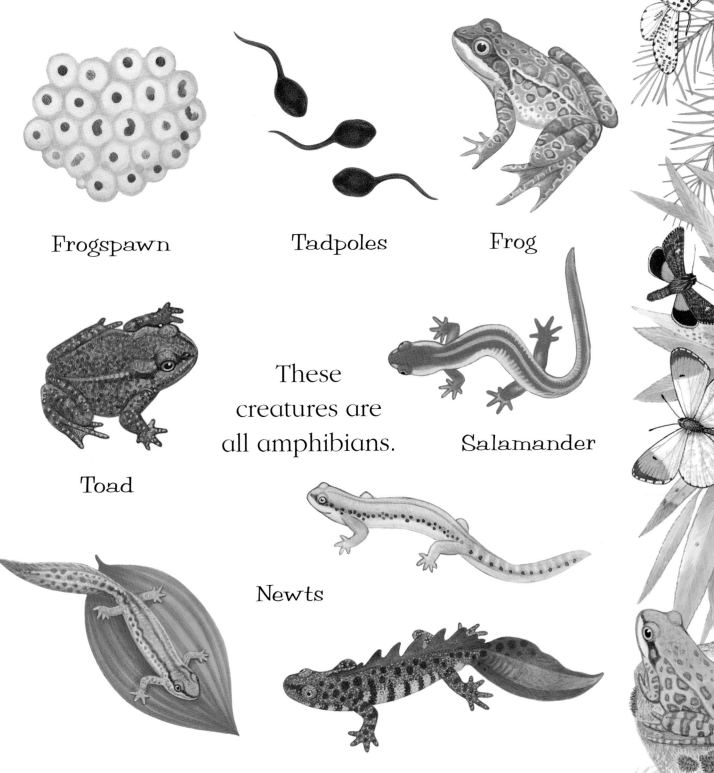

Frogspawn

Tadpoles

Frog

Toad

These creatures are all amphibians.

Salamander

Newts

All kinds of FISH

Many different kinds of fish live in ponds and rivers. Dotty Dragonfly likes to look out for them when she's flying above the water. Add two more fish to this picture from your sticker sheet.

Freshwater fish

Dotty Dragonfly's favourite fish is the goldfish. Did you know that all wild goldfish have come from pet ones that people have set free in ponds and rivers?

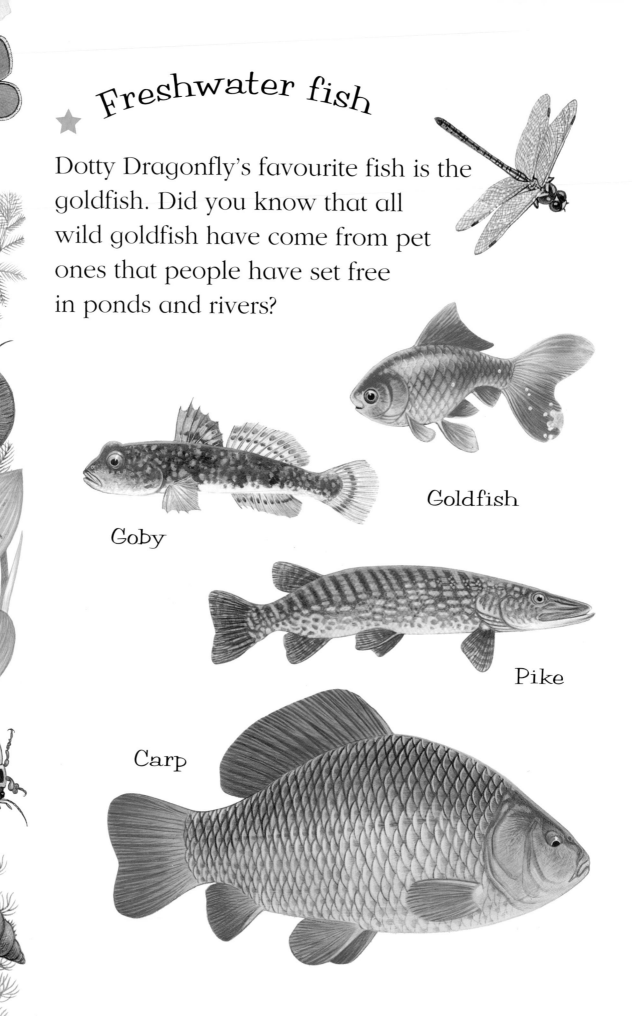

Goldfish

Goby

Pike

Carp

Use your stickers to fill in these shapes with different freshwater fish.

Salmon

Bluegill

Zander

Stickleback

Dace

All sorts of BIRDS

Little Jenny Wren is looking for some of her bird friends in the field. Use your stickers to add two more birds to the picture.

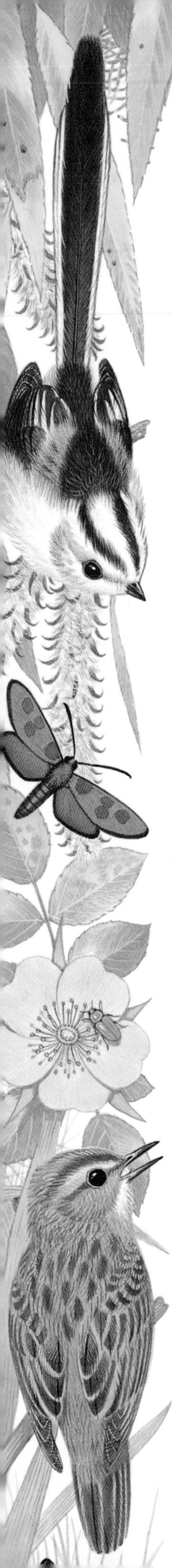

★ Feathered friends

Jenny Wren has many different
types of bird friend. They are
all covered in feathers. Make a list
of the birds that visit your garden.
Can you see any of them pictured here?

Hummingbird

Blue tit

Sparrow

Quail

Goldfinch

Use your stickers to fill in the shapes of Jenny Wren's feathered friends.

Goldcrest

Jackdaw

Swallow

Crossbill

Woodpecker

Oyster catcher

Seagull

Pigeon

Masters of the skies

Some of these bigger birds are quite rare. You might see them flying over mountains and other high ground. Now add another bald eagle and a falcon to the picture from your sticker sheet.

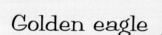

Golden eagle

Bald eagle

Hawk

Kestrel

Here are some more birds to look out for.

Barn owl

Falcon

Buzzard

Tawny owl chick

Birds who live by the water

Many birds live by rivers, ponds and lakes. Some spend most of the time paddling about in the water, even when it is freezing cold!

Goose

Kingfisher

Egret

Heron

Use your stickers to fill in the shapes with some different waterbirds.

Duckling

Duck

Swan

Cygnet

DID YOU KNOW that cygnet is the name for a baby swan?

Wood duck

All sorts of MAMMALS

Like most mammals, Billy Bunny is covered in fur. See how many furry friends he has found down in the wood. Now add a bat and a field mouse to the picture from your sticker sheet.

Mice and small mammals

Here are some of Billy Bunny's small mammal friends. They are often hard to spot in the wild because they are good at hiding from humans!

Field mouse

Bat

Dormouse

Use your stickers to fill in the animal shapes.

Stoats

Weasel

Hare

Mole

Squirrels

More furry friends

Bobby Bear has found some bigger mammals down by the old log. Now use your stickers to add a possum and a chipmunk to the scene as well.

Wolf

Raccoon

Bear

Here are three more creatures to watch out for!

Fox

Badger

Deer

Riverbank friends

Billy Bunny has found some more furry friends down by the river. See them in the panel opposite, then use your stickers to add an otter and a water vole to the picture.

Watch out for these mammals when you're near fresh water.

Otter

Water vole

Beaver

★ All sorts of SEALIFE

On the next few pages you will find all sorts of
special creatures that are only found by the sea.
Find a stripy fish and a starfish on your sticker
sheet to add to the picture.

On the beach

Sydney Seal loves looking for creatures along the seashore and in rockpools. Use your stickers to fill in the pictures of the things he has found.

Shrimp

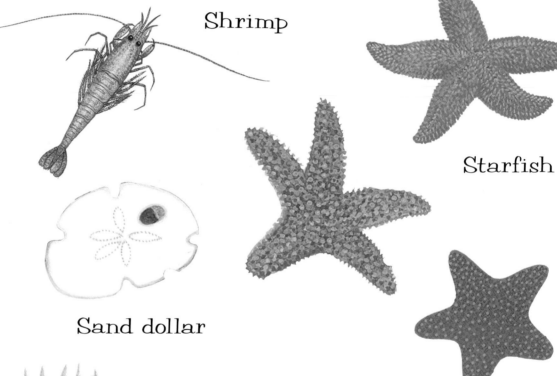

Starfish

Sand dollar

Sea fan

Sea urchins

And don't forget to see how many of the things pictured here you can find next time you go to the seaside.

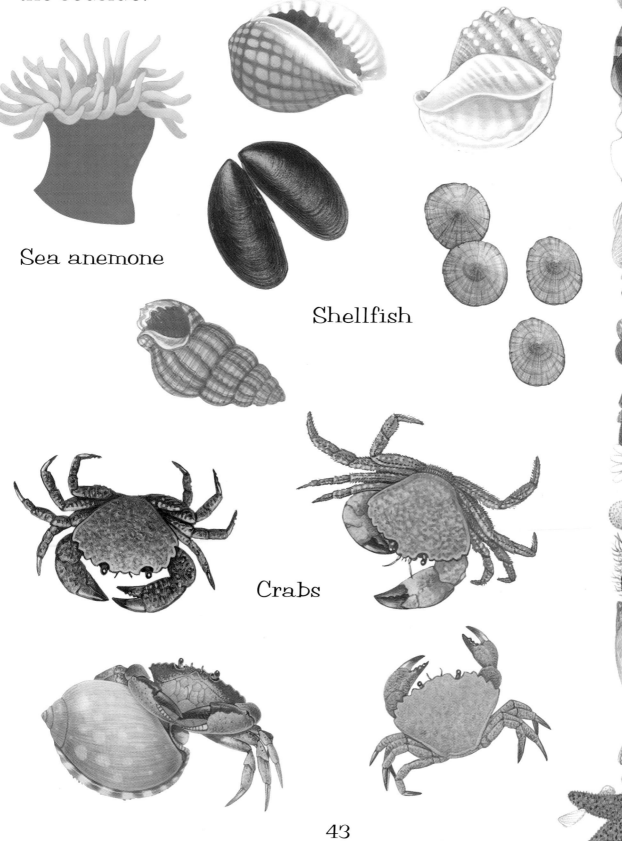

Sea anemone

Shellfish

Crabs

Under the sea!

Sydney Seal likes to dive into the ocean to find more interesting creatures. Fill in the stickers of the things he has seen beneath the waves.

Jellyfish

Seahorse

Squid

Eel

DID YOU KNOW that, although dolphins look like fish, they actually belong to the same group of creatures as I do – the mammals?

Dolphins

Look out for these fish if you ever visit
an aquarium.

Fish

Shark

★ Make your own picture!

Can you remember all of the creatures shown here? Look back in the book to find them if you can't. Now use your stickers to make up your own picture of all kinds of creatures.

How to use your stickers

Look for the page numbers on the sticker sheets to help you find the right stickers for the different activities in this book. Peel each one carefully from its backing sheet and use it to fill in the shapes or add to the pictures. You can also use your stickers to record the animals you see in real life. Watch out for the creatures in this book when you're out and about, then fill in their sticker shapes as you see them. Some animals are easier to spot than others. Some may not live where you do so look for them when you visit the zoo or travel abroad. Soon you'll find your whole book is complete. Then you'll be a champion sticker collector!

Add to scene on pages 6-7   Page 8

Page 9

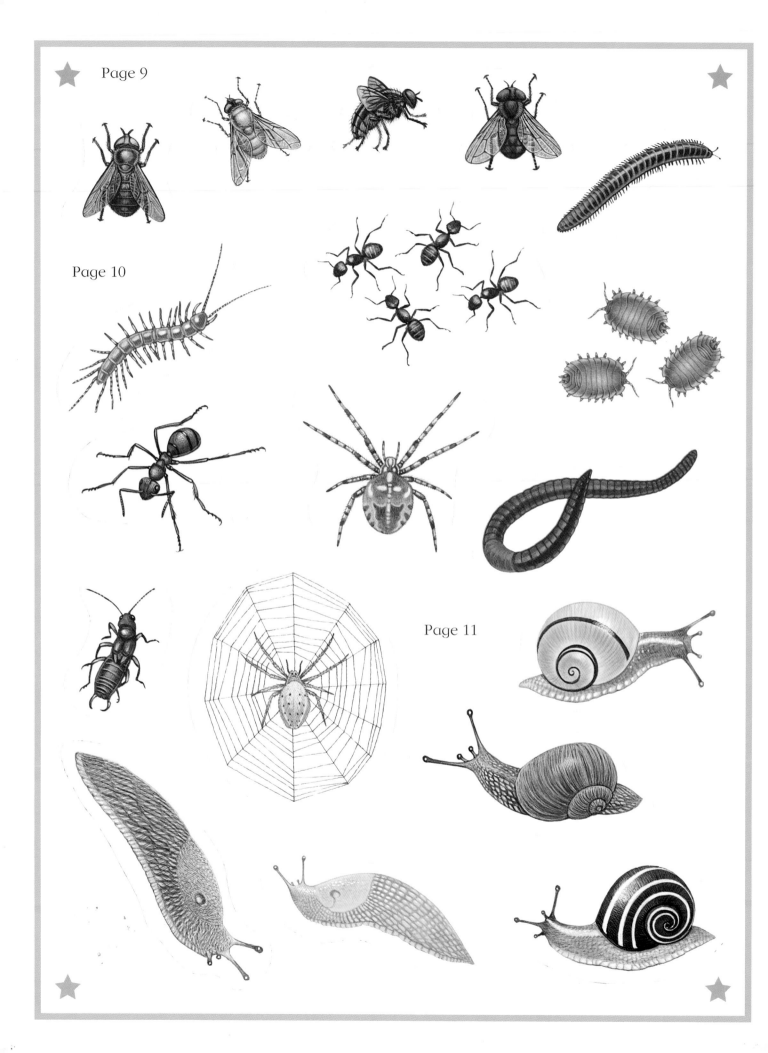

Page 9

Page 10

Page 11

Page 11

Page 12

Page 13

Add to scene on pages 14-15

Add to scene on pages 16-17

Page 18

Add to scene on pages 20-21

Add to scene on
pages 20-21

Page 22

Page 23

Add to scene on
pages 24-25

Page 26

Page 27

Page 27

Add to scene on
pages 28-29

Page 30

Page 30

Page 31

Add to scene on pages 32-33

Page 34

Page 35

Add to scene on pages 36-37

Chipmunk

Possum

Add to scene on pages 38-39

Add to scene on
pages 40-41

Add to scene on pages 40-41

Page 42

Page 43

Page 44

Add these stickers to the scene on pages 46-47